EYE ILLUSIONS™

Written by Jim Anderson
Book Design by TXF Graphics

Modern Publishing
A Division of Unisystems, Inc.
New York, New York 10022
Printed in the U.S.A.

INTRODUCTION

Welcome to a new world! Hidden within the beautiful abstract pictures in this book are exciting three-dimensional images. All you need to do is look at the pictures in a special way, relax, and the images will unfold in front of you as if by magic. You will see images of animals and toys, people and things — all in brilliant color and sharp detail. You might even be tempted to reach out and touch them.

The wonderful images in this book are called "stereograms." They are flat, two-dimensional pictures that, when viewed in the right way, appear to have three dimensions. Early 3-D pictures were really two images, and you needed special glasses or a special viewer to look at them. Thanks to modern computer technology, stereograms are now single images that can be viewed directly by anyone!

For hundreds of years, scientists have been studying how vision works. Artists began using this knowledge to draw 3-D pictures over 150 years ago, but since they drew by hand, it took them a long time to create even one image. The development of computers changed everything. Starting in the 1960s, artists used computer graphics to create ever more complex and beautiful 3-D art. At first, the 3-D images were simple shapes and designs. As computer graphic technology improved, and as the artists grew in their craft, more detailed and exciting pictures were created.

We can see these pictures in three dimensions because all human beings have "binocular" vision. Our eyes are several inches apart, so each eye sees things from a slightly different angle. This information is combined in the brain to give us a 3-D view of the world. Things not only have height and width, they have depth as well. Stereograms, though they look like simple abstract patterns, actually contain all the information the brain needs to "see" a 3-D image. The information for the right eye is on the right side of the picture, and that for the left eye is on the left side. By relaxing the focus of our eyes, we allow the two sides to overlap, and the brain is "tricked" into seeing a 3-D picture. It's a simple idea made possible thanks to complex technology. Truly, these 3-D pictures show us a new world!

INSTRUCTIONS

To see these 3-D images, you need the right setting. First, find a quiet place with bright lighting, and make sure the picture you look at is evenly lit. Then sit up straight, take a deep breath, and relax. This is very important. The more relaxed you are, the easier it will be to find the images, and the more fun you will have. Also, be patient, especially in the beginning. It may take several minutes before you can see the picture in

three dimensions. So take it easy and don't give up.

There are several ways of viewing the 3-D images in this book:

Method One

Begin by looking at the cover picture. The cover is shiny, and you should be able to see your reflection, or the reflection of a light in it. Look at the picture on the cover, but focus your eyes on the reflection. This will make your eyes relax and go out of focus. Stare at the picture for a minute or two until you "feel" something start to happen. Just relax, continue staring, and the 3-D image will appear.

Method Two

Another way to see the 3-D image is to bring the picture right up to your nose. Don't try to see the image — just let your eyes go completely out of focus. Then, while keeping your eyes out of focus, move the picture back to about arm's length. Keep looking at it with your eyes relaxed, and after a little while, the 3-D image will "pop" out.

Method Three

A third approach is to try and "see through" the picture. Look at the page, relax your eyes, and imagine you are looking "beyond" the book. Keep looking for a few minutes. Remember, patience is important. So is relaxation. Just take it easy and enjoy yourself. In time, a beautiful 3-D image will appear to you.

These three methods make up the "parallel-viewing" technique. There is also a "cross-eyed" technique that is more comfortable for some people.

Method Four

To view the images in the cross-eyed way, bring your finger, or a pen or pencil, up close to your eyes. Focus on the finger, pen or pencil. As you hold this focus, look at the stereogram. It may take a few minutes, but the 3-D image will appear. Once you develop one technique, try to develop the other. Sometimes, different techniques allow you to see slightly different images in the same stereogram. For example, if you look at a 3-D image of birds flying in the sky, the parallel-viewing technique may show you the birds in front, with the clouds in the background. With the cross-eyed technique, however, you may see the clouds in front, looking as if the birds have already flown through them leaving bird-shaped holes!

There are 14 images in this book, each with a riddle to help you discover what it is. If you're patient and keep at it, you will soon be able to see all of them. Then you truly will be an expert in the world of 3-D!

Opposite: *Nobody is as busy as this insect. All day long she goes from flower to flower, collecting delicious nectar. Then she goes home to her sisters, and together they make something delicious and sweet. This is one family that loves to "be" together.*

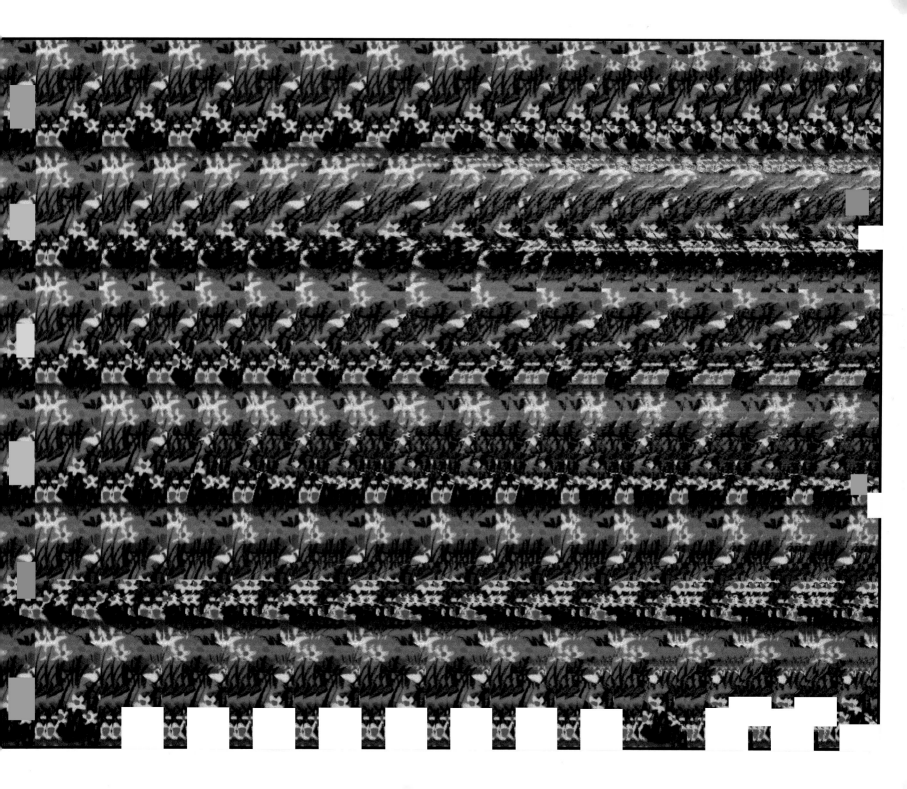

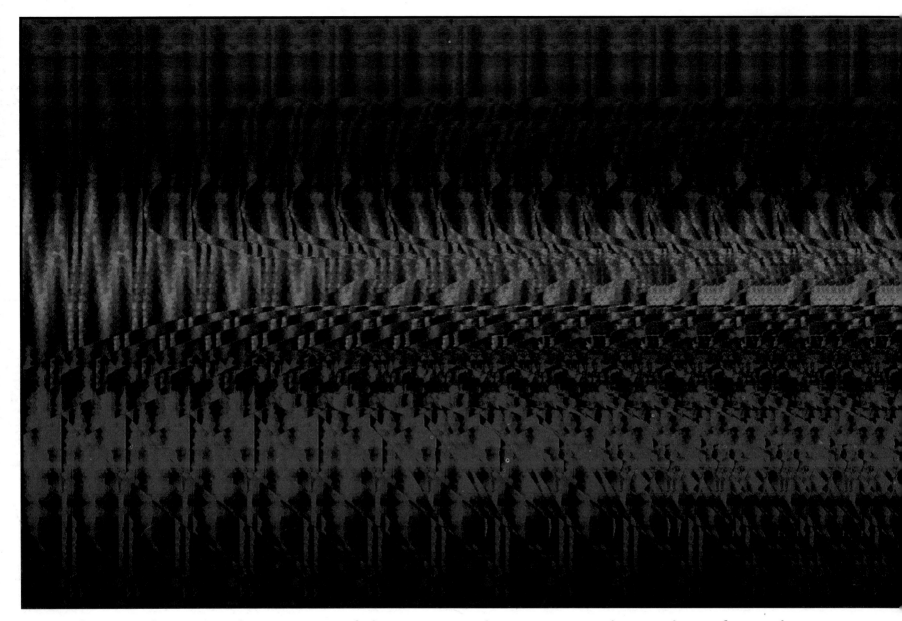

It lives in the water, but it's not a fish. It's green, but it's not a plant. It hops from place to place, but it's not a rabbit. It feasts on flies, but it's not a spider. Sometimes you can hear it singing all night long, but it's definitely not a musician or a rock star. What is it?

There's only one way to go for this athlete, and that's down. Sometimes she goes faster than a speeding automobile. One mistake, and she's in trouble. But if she falls, at least there's plenty of soft stuff for her to land on.

These animals just love "hanging around" all day. But they're out and about at night, looking for food and fun. Even though they're movie stars, most people are afraid of them, but they're really quite harmless. They'd much rather bite a fat, juicy insect than a jugular vein.

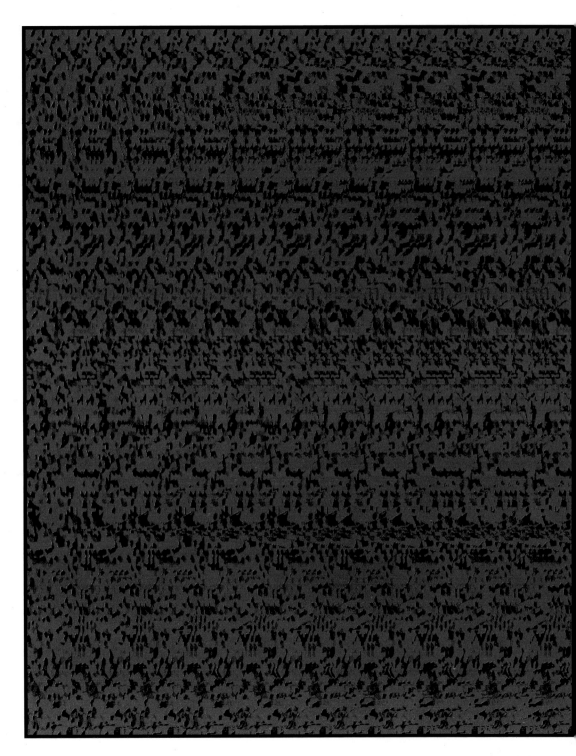

It's hard work raising a family. Seems like the kids do nothing but eat, day and night. And the noise! They're always squawking about something. Trouble is, before you know it, they'll grow up and fly away. Talk about the "empty nest" syndrome.

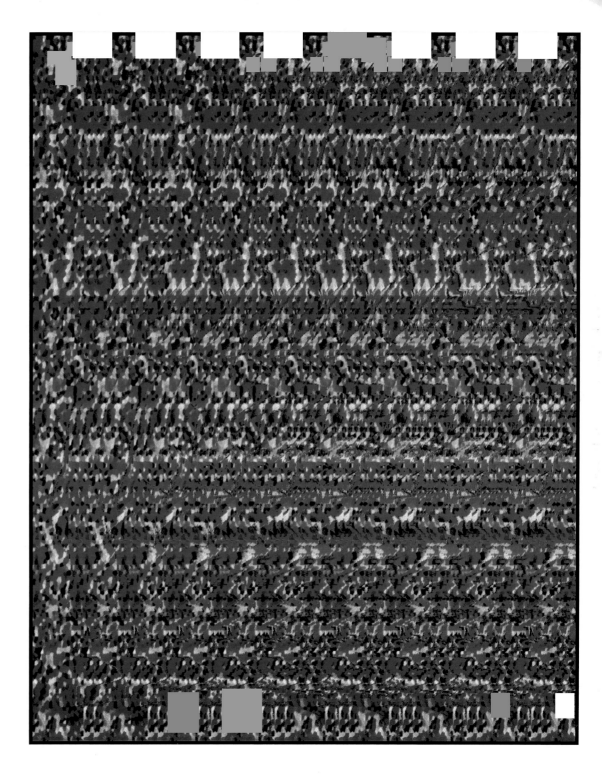

Do you want to come to "school" with us? We're very sociable, and usually travel in groups — sometimes hundreds at a time. But you won't see us on the roads. We live underwater, so if you want to join us, you'll have to put on flippers and a face mask.

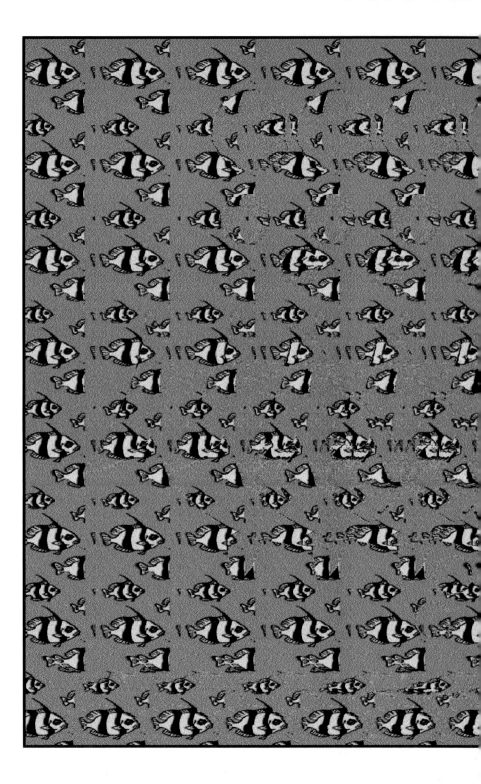

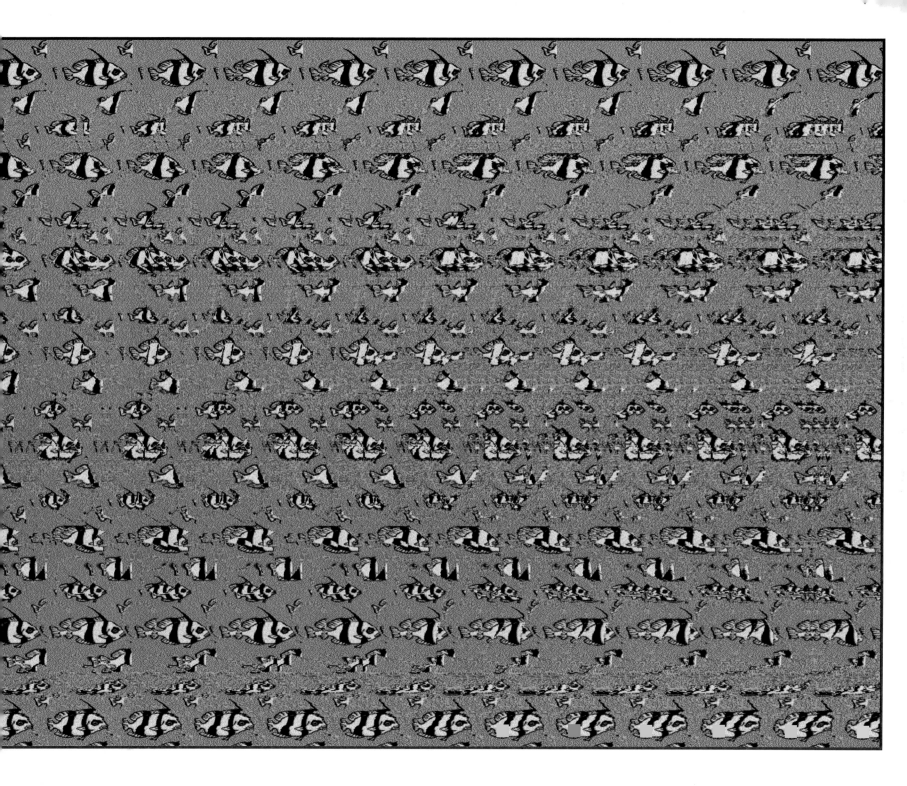

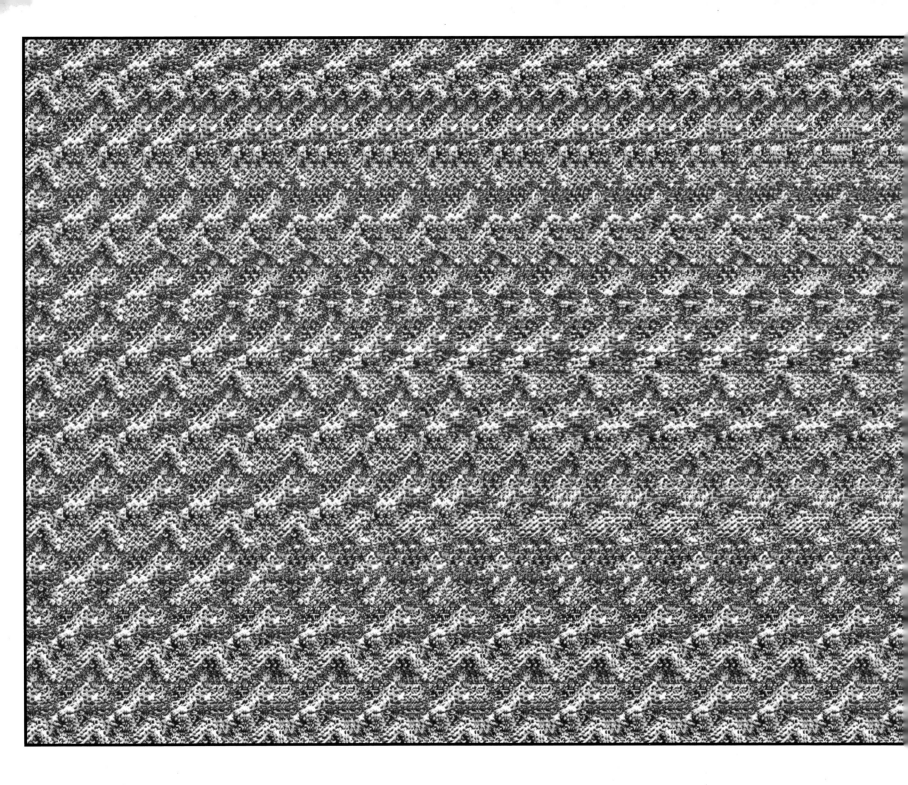

Opposite:
*Look up! You won't see me on the ground.
I spend the day among the clouds, without
a care in the world. My eyes are so keen, I
can spot my breakfast miles away. There's
nothing like a fresh fish to make me
happy. I'm so proud and free and strong,
I'm the symbol of a great nation.*

Overleaf:
*This is a workhorse, a real
jack-of-all-trades. Builders use it to carry
construction materials. Farmers use it to
haul produce to market. Families use it to
drive to the beach. Rain or shine, day or
night, this is ready to roll. If you're feeling
down, this is sure to give you a "pickup."*

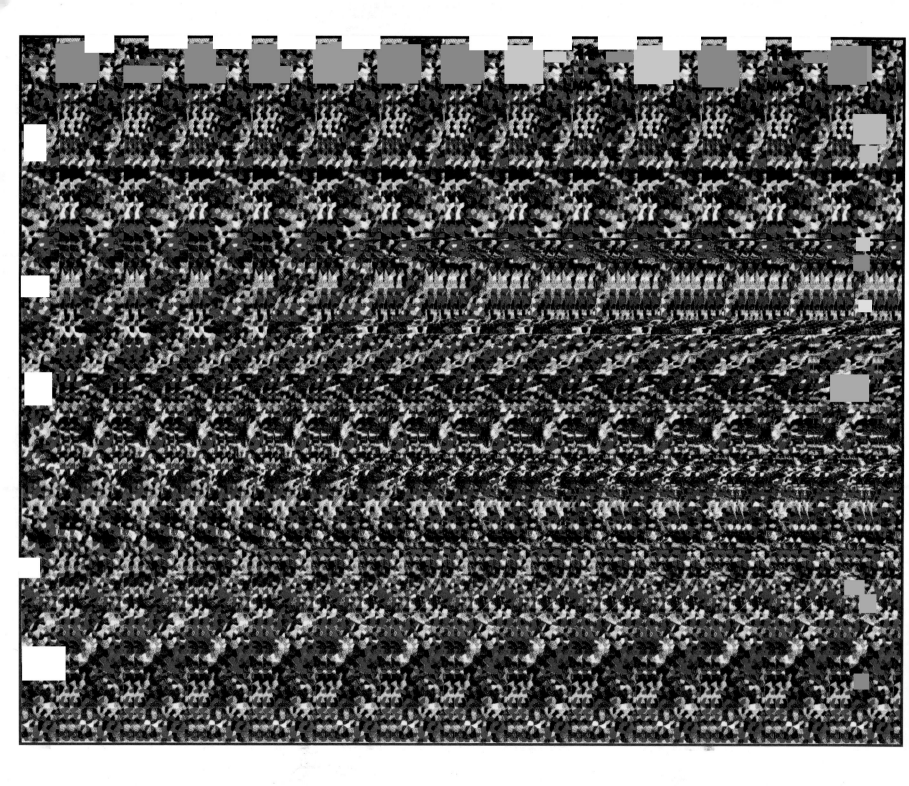

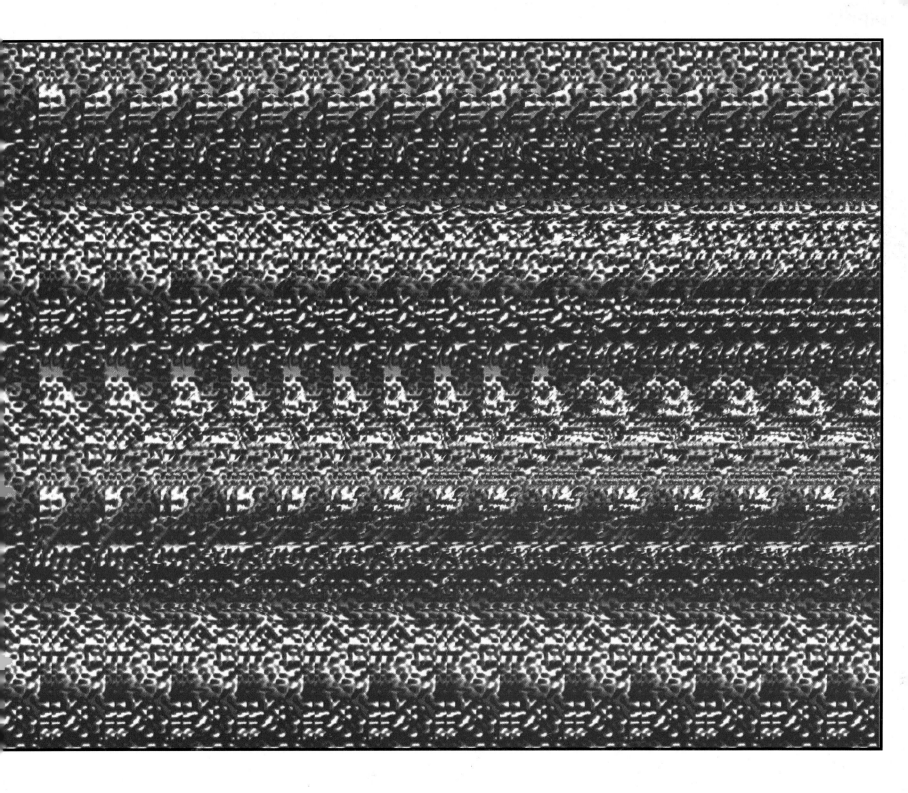

Previous page:
You need a telescope to see this, but it's worth the effort. This planet is so far away, it takes hours for a beam of light to get here from there. Is it lonely? Not at all. It has many moons to keep it company, and there's always someone to give it a "ring."

Opposite:
He looks slow, but he's steady, too. Once upon a time, he won a famous race because he just wouldn't give up. He likes the weather hot and dry, so you'll usually find him in the desert. He lives for a long time, so he's in no hurry to go anywhere. But don't challenge him to a race — he might win again!

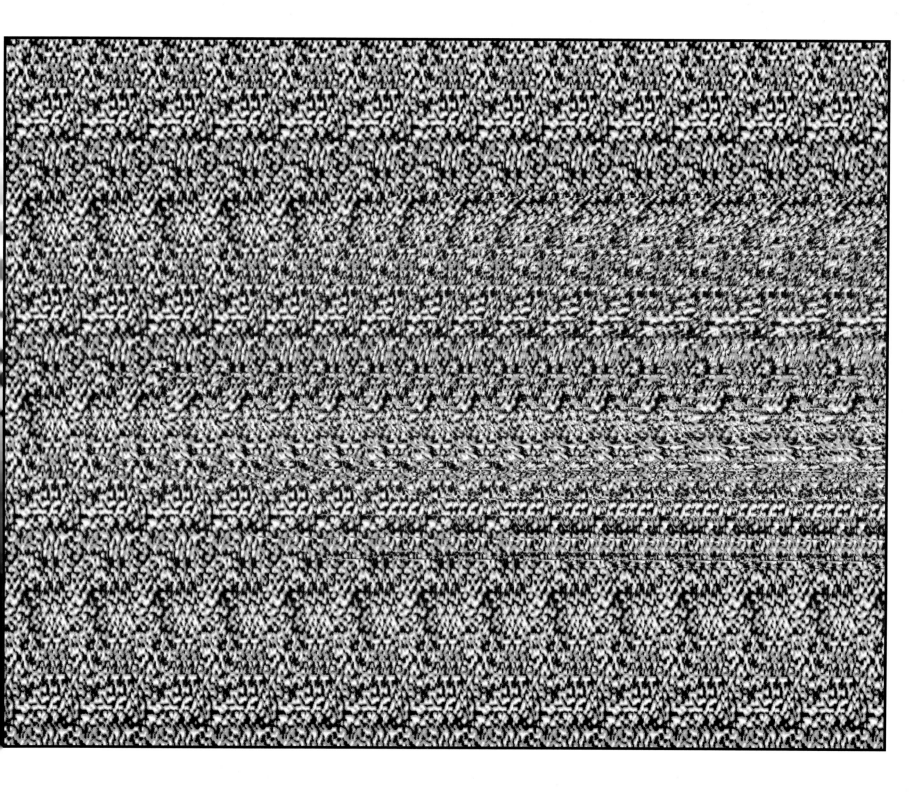

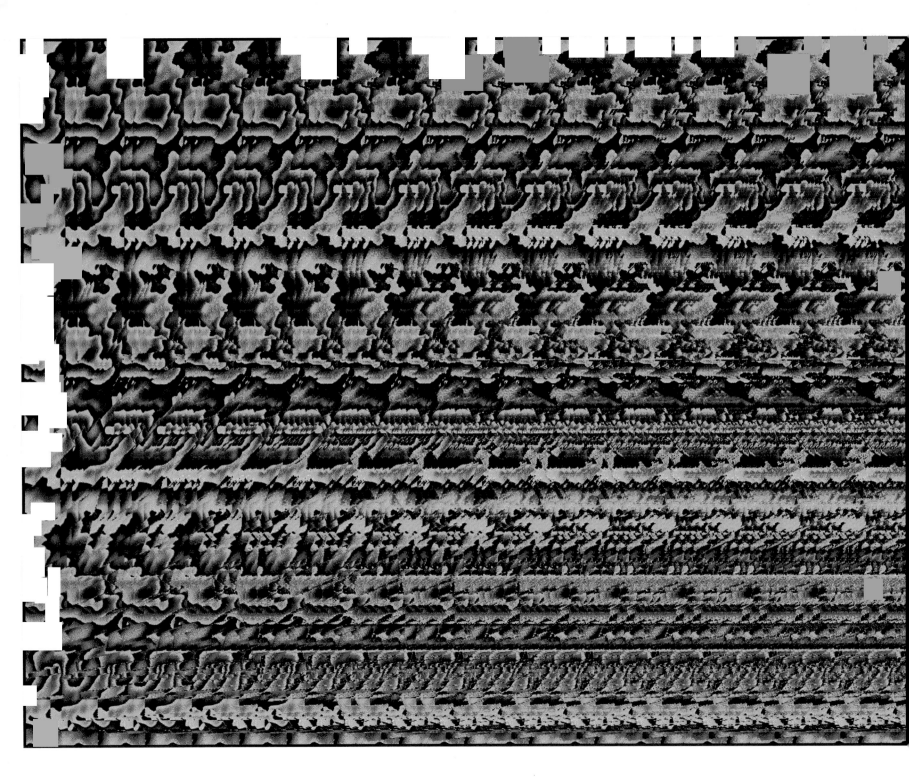

Opposite:
Don't be afraid. You can step into her parlor anytime and not get eaten. For one thing, you're much bigger than she is. Anyway, she'd rather eat a juicy bug. Flies are her favorite, and she never has any trouble making them stick around.

This is one sport where you need a suit of armor to play. Once you get the ball, eleven big people try to jump all over you. Ouch! No wonder you have to wear padding and a helmet. Best thing to do is keep running until you're in the end zone.

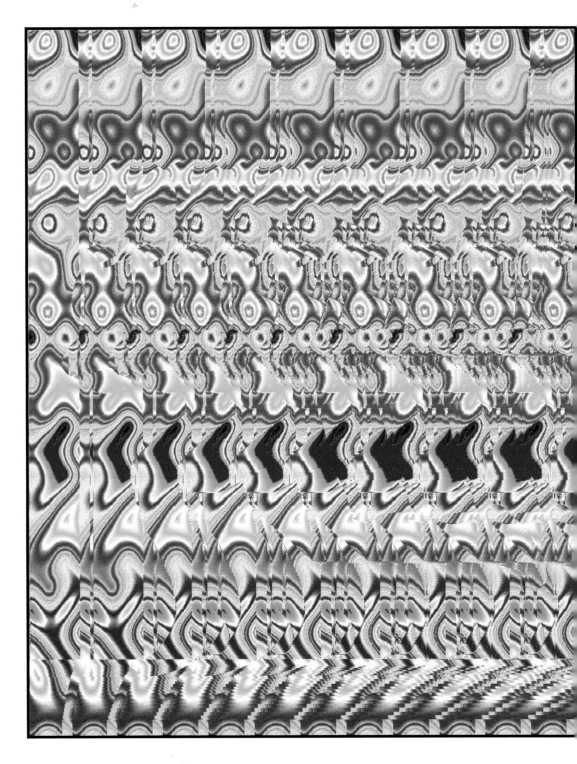

It flies, but it's not a bird or an airplane. It comes in many shapes, and is very easy to make. All you need are sticks and paper, and a long string. Take it to the park, wait for a good breeze, and off it goes. Keep holding the string, though, or you may never see it again.

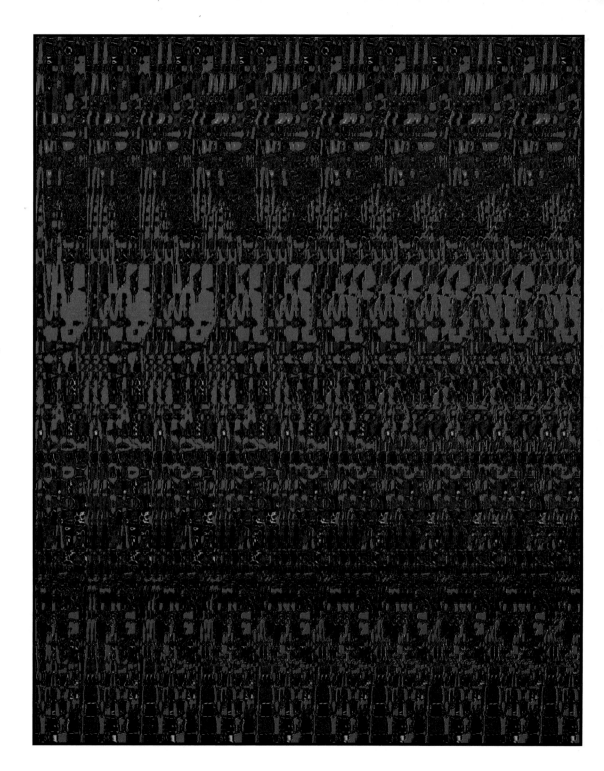

He may look awkward on land, but in the water he's graceful as a swan. He's big and strong, too, with two big teeth to frighten his enemies. Usually he's peaceful, though, and is happy just to eat lots of fish and lie in the sun on a warm rock.

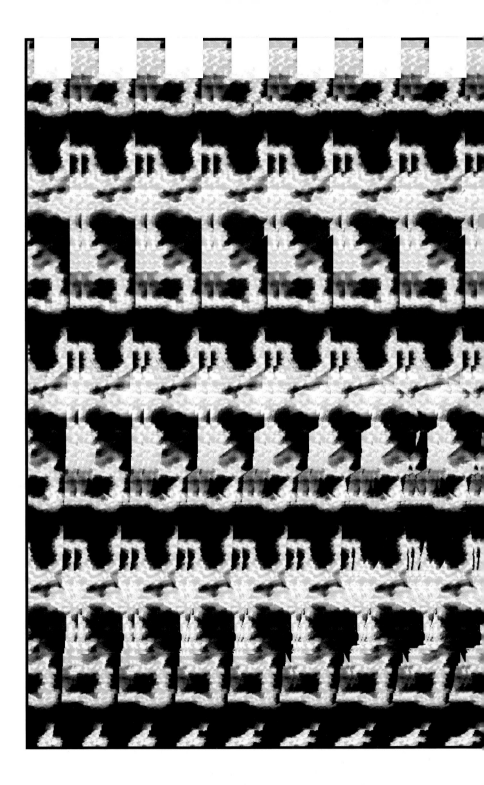

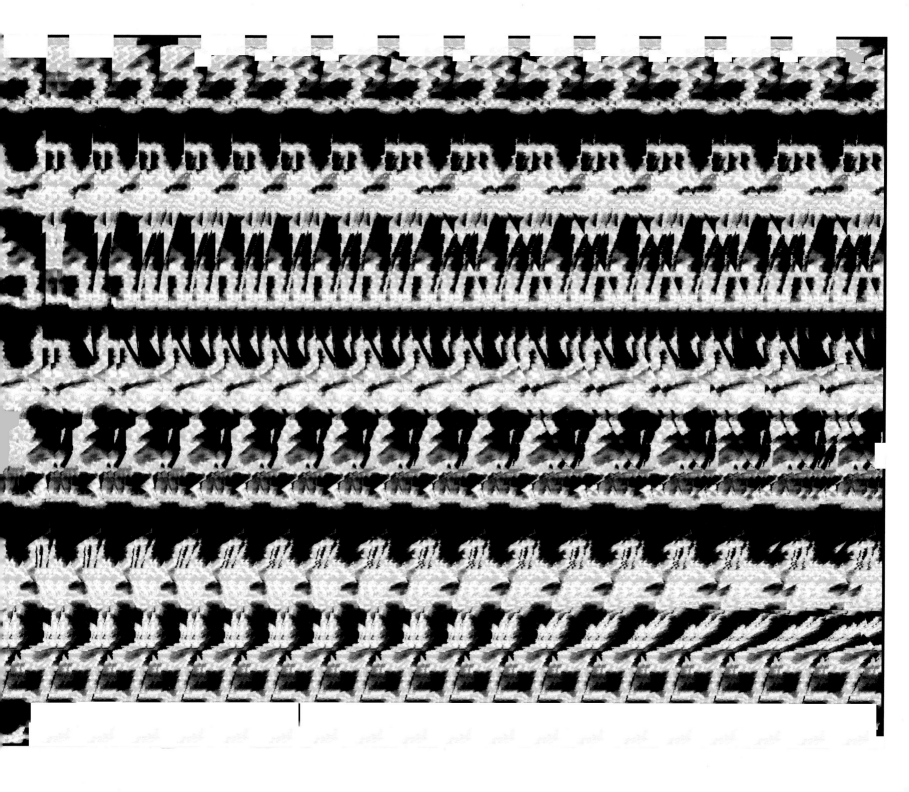

page 5　　Bee

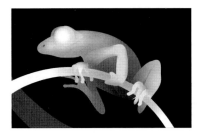

page 6　　Frog

page 7　　Skier

page 8　　Bats

page 9　　Birds

pages 10–11　Fish

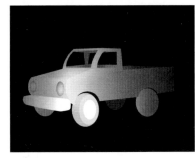

page 12　Eagle

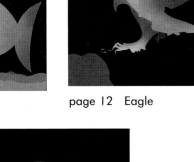

page 14　Pickup truck

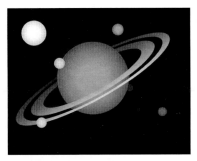

page 15　Saturn

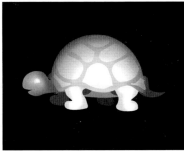

page 17　Tortoise

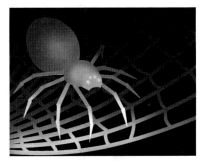

page 18　Spider

page 20 Football Player

page 21　Kites

pages 22–23　Walruses